REVERSE MEMORY LOSS

Max Kline

Reverse Memory Loss
Laurie Stewart

Copyright © MMV de Swartes Ltd, London

Published MMXII by The Windsor Group,
Hamilton House,
2 Station Road,
Epping
CM16 4HA

Copyright © MMXII The Windsor Group (This Edition)

Typeset by SJ Design and Publishing, Bromley, Kent

ISBN 978-1-903904-51-0

Contents

Notice To Readers

Chapter 1

The Memory

Why is it that we never forget how to ride a bicycle, drive a car or type a letter?

How is that we can remember a detailed experience or story from the past?

What is it that enables us to remember the words of a complicated piece of poetry or particular phrases of old and very long songs?

'Memory is the retention of, and ability to recall, information, personal experiences, and procedures (skills and habits).

'There is no universally agreed model of how memory works. Nevertheless, a good model for how memory works must be consistent with the subjective nature of consciousness and with what is known from scientific studies. Subjectivity in remembering involves at least three important factors:

- ❏ Memories are constructions made in accordance with present needs, desires, influences, etc.
- ❏ Memories are often accompanied by feelings and emotions.
- ❏ Memory usually involves awareness of the memory.'

(*Schacter 1996*)

HOW DOES OUR MEMORY WORK?

We do not know exactly how memory works, though there are many explanations for memory. Some identify memory with brain functions. For example, memory diminishes with age because neurons die off as we get older.

We remember by association. Each tiny bit of information within our memories is joined to other pieces of information, in one way or another. For instance, if someone says to you, let's go for a walk, you immediately think of perhaps putting on a coat, changing your shoes, taking the dog with you; where you are going to walk; if you have been there before. You visualise the place, perhaps a river or stream, ducks on the river. Maybe you think you will take a piece of bread to feed the ducks.

If someone says the word 'pear', you think of its shape; that it is sweet; a pear tree; perhaps a friend; fruit. But it is doubtful whether you would think of the friend unless there was some funny incident connected with a pear.

If someone asked you where the letter 'P' came numerically in the alphabet, it would be highly unlikely that you would know, without thinking about it.

You would probably count the letters in your mind, even on your fingers, as you said the alphabet to yourself, and reach 16, as P is the 16th letter. You would get to the 16th letter because you learned the alphabet as a child, therefore, you know that A is the first letter of the alphabet, the same as you know that Z is the last.

There are ways to overcome some losses of memory and loss of memory is a fact of nature. There is also growing support for the belief that exercising the body and the brain tend to preserve the neurons in the brain. 'Use it or lose it' turns out to be literally true for brain cells.

WHY DO MOST OF US HAVE A BAD MEMORY?

Most of us have brilliant memories, but we do not practise using them efficiently. Usually because we are too busy – not enough time, as we speed through our usual routines. Or, we decide we would rather do something else.

The medics of thirty years ago, maybe less, told us that senility was the cause of having a bad memory. That a bad memory was just old age and because the arteries hardened. It was just the normal ageing process – an ageing brain. However, now the medical profession are closer to understanding the causes of the major neurological disease of old age, the ageing brain, of which one of the many symptoms is a failing memory. As the brain ages, mental and physical functions are impaired.

Our bodies change as we grow older; you only have to look at old photographs to see that's true. However, as the outside of the body grows older, so does the inside and that includes the brain. From our early twenties the brain begins to lose cells, but don't panic, we only use a very tiny percentage of our brains anyway! With age the brain produces fewer chemicals, the chemicals to make it work as efficiently and without trying too hard. Over a long period of time this not quite so efficient production of chemicals can affect the way our brain stores its information and is retrieved. It seems that the loss of brain tissue with men is almost three times faster than with women.

Scientists are not exactly certain of the connection between ageing and memory, but it is apparent that there are things we can do, regardless of our age, to keep our minds sharp. We refer to these later in this book.

Donalee Markus PhD stated: "For many people the first sign of ageing is a 'senior moment' . . . a sudden, inexplicable lapse of memory. Forgetting names or appointments, misplacing car keys or reports, not knowing why they entered a room or opened a drawer leads hundreds of thousands of Americans in their 40s and 50s to enroll in memory training courses every year. Small wonder—for many people memory loss is closely associated with more severe signs of senility, including loss of control over bodily functions, regression into infantile behaviour, reversal of parent/child roles, and loss of mental competency. The spectre of Alzheimer's disease looms large even in people who have no family history of the illness.

"Research about Alzheimer's has lead to new insights into what it takes to maintain a healthy brain or at least slow down the ageing process. Important physical factors include a diet rich in antioxidants and Vitamins A and E, regular exercise, adequate sleep, and stress-free relaxation. It's also important to stay socially active and mentally challenged."

Our memories are associated with learning and experience. These are filed away, but retained, within the memory and then recovered as and when we recall them. Memory is closely associated with learning and our ability to change our behaviour through the experiences we go through, together with our ability to acquire fresh knowledge. Memory is the retention of this information. Therefore, education and memory is the basis of our knowledge, our plans and gives us the ability to ensure we think about the past, to enable us to be placed in the current time and to envisage tomorrow – the future.

HOW DOES ALZHEIMER'S DISEASE CHANGE MEMORY?

Alzheimer's disease begins by a change taking place in the Recent memory. To begin with the person with Alzheimer's disease will remember even the tiniest details of his or her distant past but will not be able to remember how to do certain things they have been used to doing almost every day of their lives and recent events or conversations. As it progresses, this terrible disease affects every part of the memory.

However, it must be made very clear that Alzheimer's disease is not a normal part of the ageing process. It is a disease and is less common than many people think. The statistics are that 10% of people over age 65 have Alzheimer's disease. The percentage increases to nearly 50% of people over the age of 85.

Some of the signs of Alzheimer's disease are:
❑ Memory problems that are not a part of the normal ageing memory.
❑ Forgetting how to do things done many times before.
❑ Problems with learning new things.

❑ Forgetting things much more often than usual.

❑ Indecision when it comes to making choices or handling money.

❑ Frequently repeating phrases or stories in the same conversation.

❑ Not being able to remember what happens each day.

FORGETTING AND AGEING

It must be remembered that lapses of memory have many causes besides Alzheimer's. If you think you've noticed yourself forgetting things more frequently than you usually do, (because let's face it, we all forget things at times), do a double check on your life at this moment in time. What else is going on within your life? Maybe you are stressed, or bored, even depressed about something or the other. Depression can cause memory problems and is not uncommon, no matter what age you are.

Maybe you have just reached retirement. Perhaps you have moved home; it is a well know fact that a move of home is akin to the stress of divorce. It may be that you have lost someone close to you. Major life changes can cause upset emotions, far more often than we realise at times.

There is quite a difference between forgetting where you parked your car and forgetting what it looks like. There's also a marked difference between wondering where on earth you put your spectacles and forgetting you wear them.

TYPES OF MEMORY LOSS

Certain injuries and diseases within the brain cause a severe loss of memory and obstruct the ability to learn. This is known as amnesia.

Other factors that could cause partial or total loss of memory are:

❑ continuous alcohol abuse;
❑ brain tumour;
❑ encephalitis;
❑ concussion.

Brain traumas may cause loss of memory manifested in two different ways:

❑ Retrograde amnesia. The person will remember things after the trauma, but will forget facts from that moment back to months or even years before.

❑ Alternatively amnesia could cause the events before the trauma to be remembered, but events after the trauma would not be remembered. In acute cases, the person might be rendered incapable of learning any new skill. However, sometimes the amnesia only lasts for a while and is caused by a temporary decrease of the blood flow.

TYPES OF MEMORY

If you go into a room and are introduced to someone, this type of information is stored in your short-term memory. Information is filed away and stored in different parts of the memory. As to what you ate for breakfast, first thing this morning, that may be stored in the recent memory. Childhood memories and other experiences of years gone by would be stored in the remote memory.

If you think about memorising a relative's wedding anniversary and then about learning to drive a car, it has to be recognised that those incidences would be filed away in different areas of the memory.

One area of the memory, amongst other things, stores dates, historical facts and telephone numbers. It is the memory for events and facts. It is easy to build but just as easily lost or forgotten.

Another area allows us to remember how to type, drive a car, play games, and tie a piece of string.

FORGETTING AND REMEMBERING

You can't talk about remembering without mentioning forgetting. It seems that as much as we do remember, we forget even more. Forgetting is okay – not all that bad, and is in fact, natural. Just imagine if you remembered every minute detail of every second of every hour, of every day during the whole of your life, no matter what the memories are. Imagine trying to sift through all of that information for the important stuff like where you left your spectacles.

There are many reasons we cannot remember certain things. Sometimes the information gets there, but is lost before it can attach itself to the long-term memory. Other reasons include disintegration, which means that information that is not used for an extended period of time fades away. It is even possible that our brains are actually programmed to erase information that no longer appears important to us.

Not being able to remember something does not mean the information has gone forever; it can be stored there but for various reasons we are unable to reach it. There are many reasons as to why we may not be able to remember; distractions such as what is going on around us or even an error of association.

Another reason for not remembering is repression, which means that we purposely push a memory out of reach because we do not want to remember the associated feelings. For example, sexual abuse as a child.

It may be that a friend gives you their telephone number and then, within seconds, you realise you have forgotten it. Why? This is because your temporary memory is limited in its ability to remember. Anything stored in there is only for a very short time. This time can be from less than a second to a few minutes.

We have to pay attention to information placed in the short-term memory. We have to repeat it and associate it with other ideas. However, we also have the ability suddenly to remember something we have forgotten. Some people do this by thinking about what it is they want to know and purposely forgetting about the question; then suddenly the answer pops up, right out of the blue. This is because their memory retained that information in the long-term memory area of the brain. This particular area has a much better capacity for allowing this to happen.

Our long-term memories can store information for years or maybe a minute or two. This area is where we keep our general information, past experiences, rules and/or events going on in the world etc.

If we begin to realise that there may be multiple areas within the brain in respect of where we store information, rather than one area, it will allow us to understand ourselves and how our memories work. This should stop us from worrying so much when we forget something for a while.

It is also important to remember that we can do certain things without really thinking about what we are actually doing: driving a car, typing a letter, riding a bicycle.

HOW DOES AGEING CHANGE THE BRAIN?

It seems that when we reach our twenties, we begin to lose brain cells a few at a time. Our body produces less of the chemicals we need to make our brain cells work. The older we are, the more these changes can affect our memory.

Ageing may affect memory by changing the way our brains store information and by making it harder to recall stored information.

Our short-term and remote memories are not usually affected by ageing. But our recent memory may be affected. We may forget the names of people we have just met. These are normal changes.

However, 'Your brain', as Tony Buzzan states in *Harnessing the ParaBrain* 'is like a sleeping giant.' He continues to point out that we only use about 1% of it and that it can improve with age.

Aristotle, the Greek philosopher and the founder of modern science, concluded that the centre of memory was located in the heart. It was not until the Renaissance that it was realised that the centre of thought was in the head and even during the 1930s/40s the brain was considered to be a simple piece of machinery. However, Donald Hebb, from Montreal, and Jersey Konorski, from Poland, two of the major experts on the phenomenon of learning and memory in the 1940s, were the first people to believe memory should involve changes or increases of nervous circuits (neurons), that communicate to each other through junctions called synapses.

Now there have been major breakthroughs and the brain is far more understood.

For instance, if you burn or cut your finger, you ensure, or try to, that it doesn't happen again. If you walk down a road and see a group of people and to walk by them is frightening, you won't go down that road again, unless there is someone with you. If you walk on ice and the ice breaks, you do not walk on ice again or at least not without testing it first of all. So your brain has been modified because of experience.

Each brain cell is called a neuron and it has a central body with thousands of tentacles, which are called dendrites. These neurons produce electrical impulses within our brains. The dendrites contain chemicals and are the major message carriers within our human thinking process. This intricate system contributes to our behaviour and the process of the memory is explained by these electrical impulses.

Repetition when learning something new is very important, because when we have a thought it is rather like clearing our way through a dense jungle. The next time we think the same thing, the way is a bit clearer because we went that way before, therefore, each time we think the same thought the way gets clearer.

The brain is a fantastic super computer and there were comparisons made between it and the world's most powerful computer, known as the Cray. It was found that what would take our brains a minute to accomplish would take the Cray one hundred years.

Professor Rosenzweig has made known that if we stimulate our brain it grows, which is why some of the great artists worked and created until into their eighties and some like Picasso, into their nineties. So we may lose brain cells but we also generate new connections within the brain.

ALZHEIMER'S DISEASE

Alzheimer's Disease is a degenerative disease characterised by progressive mental deterioration, memory loss, and dementia. Memory and abstract thought processes are impaired. Other symptoms include depression, disorientation of space and time, inability to concentrate and communicate, loss of bladder and bowel control, personality change, and severe mood swings. Death usually occurs within 5 to 10 years as the individual becomes totally incapacitated. Nerve fibres surrounding the hippocampus, the brain's memory headquarters, become tangled and shrunken. Information cannot be properly transmitted, new memory cannot be formed, and old memories cannot be retrieved. Characteristic plaques of beta-amyloid protein build up and damage nerve cells.

There are no reliable and accurate markers, in the form of blood tests, of dementia and Alzheimer's Disease. A brain scan is helpful in marking the progression of the disease by indicating the brain's glucose metabolism rate. A test measuring electrical activity in the brain can be helpful, but not definitive. The measurement of the amount of beta-amyloid found in spinal fluid is not a definitive diagnostic tool either. Diagnosis of Alzheimer's Disease is not straightforward and rests largely on a combination of clinical findings, confirmed by a specific set of physiological changes in the brain.

WHAT ARE YOUR CHANCES OF DEMENTIA AND ALZHEIMER'S DISEASE?

While the average age of an Alzheimer's Disease patient is in the 70s, the disease begins to make its appearance years earlier (in the 40s, 50s, or 60s) in the form of mental problems such as chronic forgetfulness and difficulty in handling routine chores. During this borderline state, called mild cognitive impairment (MCI), people are not demented but they do perform worse than their peers on memory tests. Family members are the first to notice this impairment. People who meet the criteria for MCI will degenerate into clinical Alzheimer's Disease at the rate of 10-15% a year, according to Ronald Peterson, director of the Mayo Alzheimer's Disease Centre. By contrast, normal elderly people deteriorate at the rate of 1-2% per year.

If you have relatives with Alzheimer's Disease, your chance of developing Alzheimer's Disease is higher than the general population. Forty-nine per cent of relatives of Alzheimer's Disease patients develop the disease by age 87.

Chapter 2

What Affects the Power of Memory?

THE ANCIENTS

The Ancient Greeks first sketched out ideas on how to use the memory. Their rules were simple and are still used today, even within the most complex modern memory systems.

This knowledge was passed down through the medieval scholars, but with the advent of printing, almost died out. But now the art of memory has been revived.

In Greek mythology, Mnemosyne is the goddess of memory. Her union with Zeus, king of the gods, gave birth to the Nine Muses: Calliope, Clio, Erato, Euterpe, Melpomene, Polyhymnia, Terpsichore, Thalia, and Urania. The Nine Muses presided over all of the arts and sciences. Consequently this epitomises that memory is one half of all creati ity.

There are three principles of memory – Imagination, Association and Location. These have been known since ancient times.

IMAGINATION

If, for a few minutes, you concentrate on the things you remember easily and wonder what they have in common, you will realise you find them interesting. Our brains are excellent at remembering things we find interesting.

The principle here is to ensure that the things that you want to remember are interesting. It is important that you conjure up images within your mind that are bright, vivid, dynamic, amusing, perhaps sexy and definitely colourful. Give them movement, perhaps make them explosive, flashing and so on. This makes them more memorable.

Using our senses is important – sight, sound, taste, touch and smell. Many of us find that vision is our primary sense, but the thought of feeling (touch) can be even more memorable.

ASSOCIATION

People say, one thing may lead to another, and it's the same with memory association – one idea will naturally lead to another. When links are connected, then we move from one image to another with the greatest of ease. This way of remembering can be used with lists, connecting each item to the one before or the next.

LOCATION

The principle of location is derived from an ancient prescription given by Cicero and other associates, that memory images should be placed in familiar settings. This idea enables us to link images with happenings or places that are already within our memories.

Memory has always been thought of as a storehouse in which to put and from which to retrieve past experiences. In ancient times the 'art of memory' was based upon systems of places and images, as though they were imprinted on the mind as letters and numerals would be on a wax tablet.

If we experience something new our brain

cells make a modification and that reflects in our behaviour pattern.

WHAT YOU CAN DO

There are many things you can do to improve your memory, among them the use of certain mental techniques, as well as special care with nutrition and medicines.

Use your memory to the extreme. Challenge it! Learn a new skill. If you work in an office environment, take lessons in something completely different, such as dancing. If you are a dancer, learn to use a computer and how to handle various computer programs. If you are a salesperson then learn to play chess or another complicated and stimulating game. If you are in computers, learn to draw free hand and/or paint. This could stimulate your brain's neural circuits to grow.

Focus your attention on whatever is the most important and avoid other thoughts. Try various exercises in doing this, for instance: pick up a key and concentrate on it. Think of its various features: what it is made of, what it is used for, its colour, how it feels within your hand. Whilst carrying out this exercise try not to allow any other thoughts to occupy your mind while you are concentrating. At first, this may not be an easy exercise to carry out, so keep persevering with it.

Later in this book I've included exercises which will teach you how to relax. Relaxing is very important when you are memorising, as it is impossible to pay attention if you are tense or nervous.

It is possible to associate facts with images, exercises further on in this book. This technique is called the mnemonic technique.

Visualisation is an important way to remember, see figures within your mind. Imagine going to a café and ordering fish and chips. See them on the plate, look at the different shapes, smell the food. Imagine eating it and if possible the taste.

Certain vitamins are essential for the memory, such as thiamine, folic acid, and B_{12}. These are found in bread and cereal, vegetables and fruits. Certain herbs are also reputed to be good for the memory: more details are given later in this book.

Water is reputed to help maintain the memory, especially in older people. According to Dr. Trukington, lack of water in the body has an immediate and deep effect on memory; dehydration can generate confusion and other thought difficulties.

Sleep is essential for maintaining a good memory. It is important that we allow the brain to have enough sleep and rest. Whilst sleeping, the brain proceeds to revise and store memory. Not to be able to sleep would produce chronic fatigue and in turn would deter the ability of concentration and the storing of information.

It is said that certain medicines cause loss of memory: tranquilisers, muscular relaxants, sleeping pills, and anti-anxiety drugs, particularly the benzoadiazepinics that include the diazepan (valium) and the lorazepan. Some medicines for the control of high blood pressure (hypertension) may cause memory problems and depression.

Alcohol can have a detrimental effect on your memory. It interferes especially with short-term memory, which impairs the ability to retain new information.

It is already well known that smoking lowers the amount of oxygen reaching the brain, and this can affect the memory. Studies have shown that, when compared with non-smokers, people smoking one or more packs of cigarettes a day had difficulties remembering people's faces and names in a test of visual and verbal memory.

Caffeine can help you maintain attention and overcome sleepiness, but the excitation promoted by these drinks may interfere with the memory function.

TEST YOUR MEMORY

Create about fifty (less if you wish) flash cards on a subject in which you may be interested but know little about, such as a new language. On one side of the card write a question and on the other side, the answer. Mix the cards up, question side up. Shuffle and pick a few of the cards. Read the question and then check to see if you have the answer correct. Or if you prefer, write the answers down and check them later. Then go over them again, this time trying to get all the correct answers.

THINGS TO HELP YOU REMEMBER

Develop a system of reminders and cues

Information comes at you from all

directions, all the time. Sometimes it's necessary to take extra steps to remind yourself of what's important. Work through the information overload with these memory triggers:

- ❑ Write it down.
- ❑ Establish a routine. Store easy-to-lose items in the same place.
- ❑ Buy a special notebook and keep a list. More than one list, if necessary
- ❑ Keep a diary, use calendars and make lists
- ❑ Complete tasks in the same order. Change is difficult and takes extra effort.
- ❑ Make links to connect things within your mind, such as using landmarks to help you find places. I have known people who found their way around by remembering the names of public houses, inns, hotels, etc.
- ❑ Put important items, such as your spectacles or keys, in the same place every time you put them down.
- ❑ Repeat names when you meet new people, or remember something significant about them. "To help remember a person's name, I'll work it into the conversation several times after being introduced", says Dr. Takahashi.

"Repetition ingrains the information in your mind. It's a great habit to get into because it works.

❑ Do things that exercise your mind and body.

❑ Run through the alphabet in your head to help you think of words you're having trouble remembering. 'Hearing' the first letter of a word may jog your memory. Many people do this little exercise.

WHAT ABOUT WHEN I KNOW A WORD BUT CAN'T RECALL IT?

This is usually just a glitch. You will usually remember the word with time. This may become more common as you get a bit older, but it's not usually serious.

HOW CAN I TELL IF MY MEMORY PROBLEMS ARE SERIOUS?

If you sometimes forget a name, then this is probably all right. The problem becomes a little more serious if you have difficulties in remembering how to do things you've done many times before. For example, going to a place you've been to quite a few times previously, or perhaps making a recipe. A memory problem is serious when it affects your daily life.

Another variation between normal memory problems and dementia is that normal loss of memory doesn't get a lot worse over a period of time. Dementia gets far worse over several months to several years.

If you are unsure if you have a serious problem then talk to your family doctor about any concerns you may have. Your doctor might be able to help you if your memory problems are caused by a medicine you're taking or by depression.

DEPRESSION

Research shows that depression may cause some forms of memory loss. When depression is treated, cognitive function, including memory, improves. The earlier symptoms are recognised, the more likely the deterioration can be slowed.

OVER-MEDICATION AND DRUG INTERACTION

The average person aged 65 is likely to be taking between 8 and 10 different prescription and/or over-the-counter drugs. Drug interactions, coupled with a nutrient poor diet, often results in mental symptomatology in addition to physical problems. Chronic alcohol abuse can lead to symptoms closely resembling Alzheimer's Disease.

DON'T BE ASHAMED

There really is no reason to be ashamed of forgetting things. Forgetting is a natural observable fact. It is essential that we do forget. In fact, the reason we forget is that our brains are organised to do away with anything that might clutter them up for no particular reason.

We mainly forget the things that were not programmed firmly enough in our nerve cell network.

Chapter 3

How to Exercise your Memory

Exercising your memory can strengthen it. Reading is a very good of way exercising the memory, because it makes us apply our attention. In addition to that, we use our eyes and our imaginations to create pictures, within our minds, as we read. Our brains organise information. All of this is essential for a good memory.

It is important to pay attention. If you think about it, you will realise that if something catches your interest, there is no difficulty in remembering it. You remember things of extreme interest without having to use repetition for the material to be memorised.

HOW SLEEP CAN STRENGTHEN THE MEMORY

Psychologically, forgetting is the temporary or permanent inability to retrieve a piece of information or a memory that had previously been recorded in the brain.

Amnesia is different from forgetting because it is thought to be normal. Forgetting involves specific bits of information. Amnesia affects a relatively broad grouping of memories or wipes out an entire segment.

Retrieving a memory depends on many factors, which include how well you have been sleeping and how well you labelled it in the first place.

People say that sleep recharges the batteries. It is a mysterious occurrence, but one of sleep's functions appears to be to merge the memory traces stored in the brain during the day.

There is an increase in the amount of rapid eye movement in both animals and humans, whilst asleep, especially when sleep follows a learning experience. On the other hand, lack of sleep adversely affects our capability to learn.

Low-frequency sleep occurs mainly at the

start of the night, and it also appears to play a role in linking memories. Certain information suggests that both major phases of sleep are involved, and that it is the alternation of low-frequency sleep with deep sleep that produces a beneficial effect. If you take sleeping pills, it will not help your memory because you won't dream for as long as you will without them. Dreaming is thought to be exceptionally important in respect of remembering.

THREE MEMORY SYSTEMS

In the 1960s, the distinction between various types of memory according to their duration was the subject of fervent debates. Certain scientists felt that the most stylish way to account for the data available at the time was to concentrate on memory as a single system of variable duration. Little by little evidence was accumulated to suggest the existence of at least three distinct memory systems.

Though the mechanisms of these three systems differ, they do link naturally from one to the other and can be regarded as the steps which form remembering – a lasting memory.

According to this concept the stimuli

detected by our senses can be either ignored, in which case they disappear almost instantly, or become apparent, in which case they enter our sensory memory. The sensory memory does not require any conscious attention, as information is stored automatically. The sensory memory is essential, because it gives us the effect of the synchronisation of an object, as our eyes go from one point to another of the object's surface to observe the detail.

For instance, if the object in your sensory memory is a ball, you may or may not pay attention to it. If you do pay attention, you recognise the kind of ball it is, be it a tennis ball, golf ball, football, etc. Once you have paid attention to a piece of information, it can be passed on to your short-term memory. Your short-term memory records small amounts of information for a period of less than one minute. You can keep a piece of information in your short-term memory for longer by repeating it to yourself. For instance, a number, a number you may require again or at least until you've finished typing it out. If you do not repeat it to yourself, it will disappear from your mind in less than a minute.

SENSORY AND SHORT-TERM MEMORY

So what is the sensory memory? It is the memory that results automatically from our observations and usually vanishes in less than a second. Short-term memory depends on the attention paid to the fundamentals of the sensory memory. It lets you retain a piece of information for less than a minute and retrieve it during this time.

The working memory is a more recent extension of the concept of short-term memory. As the study of the memory has become more refined, it has become increasingly evident that the original conception of short-term memory as a mere temporary receptacle for long-term memory is too simplistic.

The working memory is used to perform cognitive processes on the items that are temporarily stored in it. It would, therefore, be heavily involved in the process requiring analysis, such as reading, writing, or doing mathematics. The working memory appears to be made up of several independent systems and this implies that we are not aware of all the information we store in it at any given time. For instance, when typing a letter, or driving a car, we perform several tasks simultaneously. It is unlikely that all of the various types of information involved are being handled by one short-term memory system.

LONG-TERM MEMORY

Our long-term memories include our memory of recent facts, as well as our memory of older facts, the latter having become more consolidated. The long-term memory consists of three main processes that take place one after the other. It encodes, stores and recalls information.

Encoding means giving meaning to the information to be memorised. For instance, you might encode the word 'orange' as being a piece of round, orange fruit, with pips. If you could not remember 'orange' immediately, then think of 'fruit' and this should help you enough to remember 'orange'. How effectively you can remember information does depend on how deeply, within your memory, you have encoded it. The process of encoding refers not only to the information being memorised, but also as to its environment, cognitive, and the emotional context. Encoding involves using memory methods for associating ideas and images.

Storage can be regarded as the active process of consolidation that makes memories less susceptible to being forgotten. It is this consolidation that distinguishes recent memories from older memories.

Recalling memories, or the retrieval of memories, whether we want to or not, involves the mechanisms of the memory that is encoded. Information is temporarily copied from the long-term memory into the working memory and used there. The more a memory has been encoded, elaborated upon, organised, and structured, the easier it is to retrieve. Therefore, we see that forgetting can be caused by failures at either or one of these stages.

Retrieval of information encoded in long-term memory is divided into the recall and recognition parts of the memory. Recall involves reconstructing the information, whereas recognition only requires a decision as to whether one thing among others has been encountered before. Recall is more difficult, because it requires the activation of all the neurons involved in the memory in question.

There are different types of long-term memory. These can be divided into explicit, implicit, and procedural. The explicit memory can also be divided into episodic and semantic memory. The actual workings of the memory and the various subsystems work together and they interact all the time.

THE EPISODIC MEMORY

The episodic memory lets us remember occasions that we personally experience at a specific time and place. It includes the meal we ate last night, or the name of an old friend, or the date of an important event.

A distinctive characteristic of the episodic memory is that we see ourselves as actors in the activities we remember. We memorise not only the activity, but also the entire scenario surrounding it, including the emotions that came into play at the time.

The episodic memory is the part of the memory that is most often affected by various forms of amnesia.

THE SEMANTIC MEMORY

The semantic memory is the part of the memory that we use to store knowledge, for instance, our knowledge of the world. It is a database that we all have and which we can access quickly and without much effort. It also includes our memory of words and their meanings. It lets us remember the names of the world's great capitals, social customs, how things function, colours and smells. It is independent of the spatial/temporal context in which it was acquired.

Since the semantic memory is a reference memory containing information accumulated repeatedly throughout our lifetimes, it is usually out of danger when people suffer from amnesia, but some forms of dementia can affect it.

The semantic memory includes our memory of rules and the concepts that allow us to construct mental representations of the world without any immediate perceptions. Therefore, its content is abstract and associated with the meaning of verbal symbols.

FORGETTING AGAIN

We all know that at times we see something and then another time we cannot see it. We miss it. We can all think of times when we were looking for something that was there, all the time, yet we looked and looked, couldn't see it and then, a bit later on, there it was. It is interesting to realise that the unconscious mind can decide what it is going to notice and what it is not going to notice. I think we have all speculated on this, wondering how the mind can undergo this experience.

With colours, we can feel them. For instance, we may feel 'blue' or 'in the pink', we may 'see red' or be 'green with envy'. These are emotional states of mind. Yet our minds can forget to put an emotion with a colour and forget the colour needed to be remembered, or even the name of the colour, because there was no need to remember at the time. We can notice many things. We can see the colour of the lawn, or the colour of a cup of coffee we drank at breakfast time. It is easy to forget something we felt there was no need to remember, yet we can all be surprised by realising we remember something there was no point in remembering. We are trained to notice certain things that others are not trained to notice.

KEEPING HEALTH IN MIND

Having searched the house from the attic to the cellar, you eventually find your glasses resting on your forehead.

You've gone to your bedroom a couple of times in hopes of remembering why you went there in the first place. You poured orange juice, instead of milk, onto your cereal. You wonder, 'Am I losing my mind?'

Memory loss is a common complaint; we all forget something at some point in our lives, usually because we have something else on our minds. However, at some point it is typically blamed on ageing. People fear that memory loss is a sign of what's in store.

Note that dementia is a mental decline advanced enough to affect daily activities. The most common form of dementia is Alzheimer's Disease and this is more than forgetfulness (see section on Alzheimer's Disease). However, only about 10 per cent to 20 per cent of people older than 65 get dementia, so most people who occasionally forget things simply have too much on their mind.

EXERCISE YOUR MIND

Just as physical activity keeps the body strong, mental exercise keeps our minds sharp and agile.

"It is important to experience new frontiers", says Dr. Takahashi. "Excitement is an important part of learning."

If we continue to learn and challenge ourselves, our brain literally continues to grow.

Regardless of age, an active brain produces new dendrites; these are connections between nerve cells that allow cells to communicate with one another. This helps the brain store and retrieve information more easily, no matter what your age.

There are many ways in which we can challenge ourselves. Have a go – write a list. Here are a few ideas to help you along the way:

❑ Learning to play the piano or another musical instrument.
❑ Playing a word game, perhaps Scrabble.
❑ Crosswords, not only solving them, but making them up.

❏ Beginning a new career.
❏ Try a new hobby, such as walking with others, or walking alone; making things, painting, biking or bird-watching.
❏ Learning another language.
❏ Staying informed about what's going on in the world.
❏ Reading.
❏ Learning poetry.

MEMORY BY ASSOCIATION

Our memory works by association. If there is no obvious association between one thing and another, it's very difficult to remember them.

So, we should actively work to create an association between two bits of information. For example, if we have to catch a train at 3 pm, we could imagine the train within our minds and notice that it has 3 carriages. Three carriages, 3 pm, that is the association. We are now far more likely to remember the time the train is going to leave the station, even when it has faded from our short-term memory.

Lane, who lives down a lane. That type of association is very easy to remember.

Lots of information is not related in any way, shape or form, so our efforts in linking things together have to be very creative. Though it is not as hard as it seems. We all learned rhymes and acronyms, as children, that helped us remember things.

Do you remember this: 'i before e except after c'?

I was taught to remember the colours of the rainbow by the rhyme 'Richard of York gave battle in vain'. The initial letters of the words in this rhyme are the initial letters of the colours in the rainbow – red, orange, yellow, green, blue, indigo, violet.

The whole idea here is to be creative and clever, although you do not have to invent a rhyme or a poem each time you need to remember something. Make a picture within your mind that links pieces of information together, preferably something unusual or silly, so it is more memorable.

You may want to remember that you left your car in Daisy Field Road. So imagine your car in a field full of daisies.

To demonstrate how well this can work read the following list of words and think of a way to link them together. Some will be easier than others:

- ❑ Dog
- ❑ Toothbrush
- ❑ Tail
- ❑ Coat hook
- ❑ Car
- ❑ Popcorn
- ❑ River
- ❑ Umbrella

This is one way of remembering the list:

You see a dog, cleaning its teeth with a toothbrush, which is on the end of his tail. His tail is still hung on a coat hook, which is fixed to a car with the back seat covered in popcorn, as it floats down the river in an umbrella.

After you have formed the associations (if you had trouble on one or two of them, that's okay; just skip them for now), cover it up and write down your list of words. The more vivid and clear your associations are, the easier you will be able to remember the list.

MORE ABOUT ASSOCIATION

A list association is a time-proven method that works and it is consistent with what psychologists have discovered about the human memory. We know that memory works best by association, and we are simply taking advantage of that property to help us remember things more easily. Following are some other properties of memory.

Law of Recently

We are more likely to remember things that happened recently than those that happened a long time ago. We probably remember what we had for dinner yesterday, but not what we ate for dinner two weeks ago today.

Law of Vividness

We tend to remember the most spectacular or striking impressions rather than those that are more ordinary. You can probably remember what you did on your last birthday, but not what happened on the previous day, unless it was another special occasion.

The 'Law of vividness?' If we wanted to memorise two words, 'table' and 'weed', we might think of digging up a weed and placing it on the table. To make it vivid, we see an orchid, which we have grown in a pot, with much love and tender care, pulled out by a much adored two year old child, who manages to say one word, "Weed", as she reaches up and puts it onto the kitchen table. This is why, when we try to invent associations, the rule is the sillier, the better!

Law of Frequency

We tend to remember things we experience the most often, rather than those we experience only once in a while. You are much more likely to remember your name or your phone number than how to say 'Bread' in German (that is unless we live there). We can take advantage of this law as well because we all know that if we repeat a word or phrase 20 times, we can remember it more easily.

WHAT IF I MEMORISE TOO MUCH USELESS INFORMATION?'

It appears that the human brain has a limitless capacity for storing information. This means that our brains will never be crammed full of information. However, new information may interfere with information learned in the past, making the older information more difficult to remember. To avoid this problem, a little 'management' may be required.

For temporary things, such as memorising the time of a doctor's appointment or the name of some person you are going to call once, but never again, do nothing. Because when we no longer need this information, we eventually forget.

For more permanent things, such as memorising trivia facts, phone numbers, license plates, etc., purposely go back over them and remember the pictures you came up with again. Repeat every few hours or so and then recall this information once a day for a few days. At the end of the week, the information you memorised will have become virtually fixed in your memory.

What about all of the silly pictures? Will our minds be cluttered up with all of them? Probably not. Think of all the pictures (things we observe normally) within a day. If we recall a piece of information often enough, eventually we will no longer need the picture to remember it.

WHAT IF I CAN'T THINK OF AN ASSOCIATION?

All of the examples given thus far have had easy associations — the association was either very obvious, or there were two words that could be pictured very easily together in the mind. But what about words that can't be pictured so easily? Don't panic, there are other techniques that can be used.

Maybe you want to remember that Mr Peter Unwin lives in Nottingham Road. Your second nature should tell you to link 'Unwin' with 'Nottingham', but neither word forms a good and easy mental picture. This means we have to find one, which can be done by finding words that rhyme or are related in some way. For Unwin we could find 'Fun Win'. For Nottingham, perhaps Robin Hood. Therefore, we could picture Mr Unwin at a race course meeting, dressed as Robin Hood, having placed a bet on a horse which is wearing a funny hat, with its ears poking through, and then see it win the race.

Chapter 4

Techniques for Memorising

NUMBERS

Research by cognitive neuroscientist Stanislas Dehaene of the National Institute of Health and Medical Research (Inserm) in Paris and cognitive psychologist Elizabeth Spelke of Massachusetts Institute of Technology has resulted in some fascinating findings on how our brains deal with numbers.

Brain scans indicate that people use different parts of their brains when doing different types of maths. Our left frontal lobes 'light up' when we make exact calculations, but our left and right parietal lobes are triggered when we make estimates and count on our fingers.

Moreover, people who have difficulty with numbers, a condition known as 'dyscalculia', are also apt to have problems conceptualising time and direction. They tend to be chronically late, easily disoriented in new environments, usually make decisions based on intuition rather than logic, have difficulty planning activities and keeping track of money. It is not a question of intelligence or memory. People with dyscalculia can be highly articulate and excellent writers and readers. The issue is the functional integration of the brain.

TECHNIQUE FOR MEMORISING NUMBERS

We live in a society filled with numbers. National Insurance numbers, telephone numbers, postal codes, dates, car licence numbers, prices, costs. Yet most of us have difficulty in remembering numbers, because they are difficult to associate. Our brains think in pictures not numbers. It is much easier for us to imagine a horse wearing a hat that it is to picture a list of numbers. However, what would happen if we could turn a number into a word and the word into a picture?

Suppose we assigned each of the digits 0 to 9 to a consonant. Then, when we want to remember a number, we convert the number into consonants, insert vowels, and form a word. This word can then be used to form an association much more readily, rather than trying to use the number itself.

Below is the standardised mnemonic system, used by memory experts. It has been optimised in order to make it easy to learn and use. Pairs of letters have been grouped together because of their phonetic similarity, such as t and d or p and b.

NUMBER	LETTER/ SOUND	MEMORY AID
1	t, d	t has one down stroke
2	n	n has two down strokes
3	m	m has three down strokes
4	r	'four' ends with R
5	l	Latin 50 = L
6	j, sh, ch	J reversed looks like a reversed walking stick
7	k, g (hard)	Visualise a K drawn with two 7s
8	f, v	Cursive f has two loops like an 8
9	p, b	P reversed looks like 9
0	z, s	'zero' starts with Z

Here are some rules about using the number alphabet:

❏ The alphabet is strictly phonetic. For example, the word 'cough' should be thought of as KoF and translated into 78; 'gem' is pronounced JeM and is thus 63. Double letters are not counted. For example, 'Butter' translates into B, T and R (only one T).

❏ Three consonant sounds do not appear in the chart: W, H and Y.

❏ Vowels are always ignored, as well as W, H and Y mentioned above.

❏ When creating words from consonants, vivid nouns usually work the best, rather than adjectives, verbs or other related words.

Before reading further, take a few minutes to memorise the number alphabet.

Write the groups of letters in random order on a piece of paper, look at the letter groups, and try to come up with the number.

TECHNIQUES FOR MEMORISING LISTS

Memorising Short Lists

If you decide to go to the supermarket and need five items, how would you remember the list? There is a simple way. Say.... you need to buy milk, bread, bacon, eggs and cheese. The easiest way is simply to 'link' the words together in a long chain, like this:

Milk – Bread – Bacon – Eggs – Cheese

Think of a story within your mind to link the five items together. For instance, imagine you are driving to the shop with your purse on the seat, by the side of you. You park your car, pick up your purse and walk towards the shop, when a pig runs across your pathway, with an egg on each ear. You look behind you and see someone rolling a cheese towards you. You wait to tell them about the pig, with an egg on each ear, when you notice this person washing his/her face with milk. You turn towards the shop again and as you reach it, you realise you are going to have to step over a pile of loaves of bread to get to the door.

Now that was quite a long story but remember, it is all in your head, you don't have to write it down on paper. You are thinking of it within your mind, so time goes very quickly. If you want to add extra details then do so. Maybe the smell of the bread. The more ways you experience an object – touch, smell, how it looks, the more likely you will remember it later on.

Having stepped over the bread, you see the pig, with the eggs on its ears, drinking a glass of milk. Notice we didn't just put all the grocery items in the bag one by one. The instances would be so similar we would probably get them mixed up! So a lot of variety was used. The story was fun and no doubt you can stop right now, look away from this book, think through the story again and remember perfectly the five items. Try it again later on today, or tomorrow and see if you still remember!

Memorising Long Lists

The list you had to remember, for groceries, was comparatively easy, but what about a long list, such as all the counties in the UK? If you forget a word in middle, the chain is broken and you've lost the rest! Also, if you want to remember the 6th county – possible if you memorised the counties in order of the alphabet or population – you would have to remember the first six. Another way to memorise lists is to use what are called 'peg words'. Before we begin, memorise this short list of peg words. Note that they are numbered, and the peg word does actually translate into the correct number,

so you should be able to form some associations right away.
1.   Hat
2.   Hen
3.   Ham
4.   Rye
5.   Hill

Practise remembering the peg words before continuing.

Now, let's use the peg words to memorise a list of five counties in England. Somerset, Cornwall, Dorset, Wiltshire, and Devon. Take each of the peg words and place them next to each item in your list of counties. Now form some simply associations between the words. Note that instead of making a huge chain, we are now working with pairs.

PEG	ITEM	ASSOCIATION
1. Hat	Somerset	Imagine a man, hat on his head, leaning on a gate, a straw in his mouth.
2. Hen	Cornwall	A hen sat on the cliffs at Land's End
3. Ham	Dorset	Ham on a doorstep
4. Rye	Wiltshire	See a piece of rye bread on one of the stones at Stonehenge
5. Hill	Devonshire	Cream cascading down the hill

After studying the above associations, cover them up and take a look at the five peg items. Can you now name all five counties on your list? Hopefully, you can. Note that we've solved our problem. Our long chain of items has been changed to a numerical chain, an easy list of 1, 2, 3, 4, and 5. Each item on the list matches up with a certain peg item, which, after a little practice, you can easily name. Finally, we associate simple pairs of words: the peg words with the actual list of items. It is possible you could have memorised it quite easily by using the short list method, but this method is easier for long lists.

To remember a longer list, you need to remember a basic set of peg words, words that are derived from their associated numbers directly. You can make up your own, but there is an example below. Use very short words for your list. Some can stand for a number. Make your list as easy as possible.

1. Hat	11. Legs
2. Hen	12. Night
3. Ham	13. End
4. Rye	14. Tore
5. Hill	15. Seam
6. Stick	16. Tissue
7. Heaven	17. Swan
8. Gate	18. Circle
9. Time	19. Ape
10. Lend	20. Duck

The peg words method for lists is great for lists of items that must be in a specific order, because peg words are tied to specific numbers. If you did memorise your initial list of five peg words, note how easily you can remember the 4th item without having to go through the others (1-3 initially). You can even exchange items in the list to come up with easier associations.

PRACTICE MAKES PERFECT

By this time you have learned a lot of different techniques for remembering things by forming pictures and making associations, using your imagination to make vivid or funny pictures. You have converted numbers to picture words. You have linked items in a long chain to form a list. You have paired items with peg words to memorise numbered lists. These are basic techniques. There are books on these subjects in respect of improving your memory.

You can apply what you have learned here, to your life now, in the effort to remember things a lot more easily.

Memorise things every day. Remembering is a bit like using a particular computer program. You are taught the basic steps. You do your lessons and read your notes carefully, but before you can use the program efficiently you need practice. To begin with it won't be that easy, but with time it is.

At the moment it may be taking you a while to think of picture words for things, and you haven't learned yet which pictures work better for you than others. Look around your life and find things to memorise, such as your library telephone number; your favourite sponge cake recipe; the few phrases of French you've always wanted to memorise; your own car number plate; your National Insurance Number; your Premium Bond numbers, etc. If you have problems with this, never give up, keep on keeping on. Work at it until you succeed.

Chapter 5

A Healthy Lifestyle

STAY PHYSICALLY ACTIVE

Following a healthy lifestyle is essential for keeping your mind healthy and your memory efficient.

Exercising every day helps make the blood flow. Certain people find exercising difficult to do alone, but get motivated when they exercise with a friend or friends. Some choose a favourite pet to accompany them on walks.

Obviously, if you have health problems you must get your doctor's approval first of all, but try brisk walking, bicycling or swimming. They are good for your heart, lungs and blood vessels which work to deliver adequate oxygen to your muscles. Exercise increases stamina and endurance; it can also decrease high blood pressure, which may reduce your risk of stroke, heart disease, kidney disease and other related conditions.

No need to overdo it, but you can increase your strength by using weights. This can slow down or even reverse the loss of muscle mass associated with getting older. It can also slow down bone loss, cut your risk of injury and make you feel more energetic.

Stretching is a great way to exercise. It increases the ability to bend and stretch your joints, muscles and ligaments and helps to get rid of stiffness and also prevents injury.

"Exercising also helps your mood," says Dr. Takahashi. "People who exercise briefly each day — maybe get some sunlight — certainly have better moods."

You will find yourself awake, more alert and quicker mentally. Exercising regularly helps us to sleep a lot better, which in turn aids our memory.

EAT, DRINK AND BE HEALTHY

Ensure that your diet is rich in fruits and vegetables because they contain antioxidants. Antioxidants are substances that protect and nourish the brain cells. These foods may also reduce your risk of cancer, high blood pressure, coronary artery disease, diabetes and osteoporosis.

Drink plenty of water. Our bodies are 7/10ths water, so water is essential to the human body. Water practically *is* the human body and lack of it leads to dehydration, which can leave us feeling tired and makes it difficult to concentrate. Therefore, it is very important to drink water. You may feel that to drink lots of water would be a bit of a nuisance. However, you can make it a sort of challenge. Look for water drinking fountains and take a sip at each one you see. Fill up a bottle with water and instead of taking a break to go and make a cup of tea or coffee, drink from your water bottle. Drink a glass of water at lunch instead of soft drinks, coffee or other beverages. It is cheaper and much better for you.

TAKE TIME TO REMEMBER THINGS

Just normal ageing changes the brain and this makes our minds slightly less efficient in processing new information.

But Dr. Takahashi accentuates that wisdom

can compensate for physical changes. "It's true that we lose some capacity for new memory", says Dr. Takahashi. However, experience compensates for this loss. "Older adults can still operate at an extremely high functional level despite physiologic changes."

Forgetfulness is often the price we pay for having too much on our minds. It can be a signal for us to slow down the pace and pay full attention to the task in hand, whatever it is.

KEEP A POSITIVE ATTITUDE

Being happy plays an enormous part in our outlook on life. It makes us more alert and in turn our senses become more open to receiving information. It seems that optimists tend to live longer.

TALK TO YOUR DOCTOR

There are many factors, which are not related to ageing or genetics, that can add to a memory problem. They include the use of certain medications, poor vision and hearing, vitamin deficiencies, tiredness, depression, stress and illnesses.

Depression in particular can cause problems

with memory and concentration and often is mistaken for Alzheimer's disease in older adults. Depression can be treated and that will improve both memory and concentration.

If you or your family worry about your memory, get evaluated. Your doctor may be able to determine whether the cause is treatable.

CHECK YOUR LEVELS

Do you know your blood pressure, cholesterol and blood sugar levels? If not, get them checked out. Ensure that your thyroid gland is functioning properly. These tests are relatively easy to take and are good indicators of what's going on inside your body. Older adults who keep a check on their blood pressure reduce their risk of having a stroke.

HEALTHY BLOOD PRESSURE

Have your blood pressure checked regularly. Blood pressure is the force of the flowing blood against the walls of the arteries. It's measured in two numbers, for example, 140/90. The first number (140) is systolic pressure, the pressure when the heart contracts and pumps the blood through the body. The lower number (90) is diastolic pressure, the pressure between pumps, when the heart is resting.

High blood pressure is often silent — or without symptoms — until a major problem develops. That's why it's essential to see your family doctor for check-ups on a regular basis. Such check-ups can literally save your life. Your doctor can help you prevent high blood pressure or, at minimum, treat it at an earlier stage when it's easier to manage.

HEALTHY CHOLESTEROL

Have your cholesterol checked by your doctor every five years — more often if you have a problem with your cholesterol level.

A variety of things can affect cholesterol levels. These are the things you can do something about:

Diet. Saturated fat and cholesterol in the food you eat make your blood cholesterol level go up. Saturated fat is the main culprit, but cholesterol in foods also matters. Reducing the amount of saturated fat and cholesterol in your diet helps lower your blood cholesterol level.

Weight. Being overweight is a risk factor for

heart disease. It also tends to increase your cholesterol. Losing weight can help lower your LDL and total cholesterol levels, as well as raise your HDL (good cholesterol) and lower your triglyceride levels.

Physical Activity. Not being physically active is a risk factor for heart disease. Regular physical activity can help lower LDL (bad) cholesterol and raise HDL (good) cholesterol levels. It also helps you lose weight. You should try to be physically active for 30 minutes on most, if not all, days.

Things you cannot do anything about also can affect cholesterol levels. These include:

Age and Gender: As women and men get older, their cholesterol levels rise. Before the age of menopause, women have lower total cholesterol levels than men of the same age. After the age of menopause, women's LDL levels tend to rise.

Heredity: Your genes partly determine how much cholesterol your body makes. High blood cholesterol can run in families.

KEEP YOUR PERSPECTIVE

You are not the first person to have placed an

item of clothing (your jacket) or a cup of tea on the roof of your car and then driven away . . . and you won't be the last. You are not the first person to dial a phone number only to forget whom you are trying to call. This sort of thing happens, it doesn't matter unless you feel you are doing it too often, but don't get too concerned. Everyone loses a bit of memory, as time goes on, but experience, from time gone by, usually makes up for what we have lost.

Everyone has difficulty remembering things at times. So don't lose sight of how much you do remember. Wisdom is built from a lifetime of memories.

Chapter 6

The Benefits of Positive Thinking

Positive thinking is a powerful tool, which you can use within your life to improve your health, happiness and memory.

Positive thinking is the process of creating thoughts and focusing energy in order to bring into your life a positive outcome, which you can see as a benefit to yourself and/or others. This is a powerful gift that we all have, but many are still totally unaware of it.

All of our feelings, beliefs and knowledge are based on our internal thoughts, both conscious and subconscious. We are in control, whether we know it or not.

We can be positive or negative, enthusiastic or dull, active or passive.

The biggest difference between people is their attitude to life. Certain people find learning enjoyable and exciting when other people, who hate learning, find it drudgery. For many, learning is okay, just something required of them in a new job.

To understand the course of action involved in positive thinking, we have to look at the dynamics of how our minds work; the way the conscious and subconscious minds interact with each other and the body; how we emotionally interact with the world within and around us.

This all involves the way we use our personal energy, expressed through our mental, emotional and physical reactions to life. To understand fully how to maximise the use of our energy, it is a good idea to read up on stress management (*see Stress Management in this book*). People waste a lot of their energy through a stress reaction to life situations.

Positive thinking takes practice. It is something that we can learn, but it takes time and patience with ourselves. We were not born with it and that is a pity. It teaches you how to train your mind and subconscious mind to become more positive so that you practise positive thinking throughout your life.

A LITTLE BACKGROUND ON POSITIVE THINKING

Many of you have probably read at least something on positive thinking, but many believe it is only something done on certain occasions. Often we hear people say, "I'm a positive thinker and things will improve, I know that." This is great – but it's not enough to create positive results within our lives.

Some say that positive thinking is not an attitude we can turn to when things go wrong, but I disagree with this wholeheartedly. No, it cannot create a miracle, but it helps us at least to try and see a positive outcome arising from a situation that is exceptionally negative. I know it cannot put things right, just like that, but it can help. It can help in respect of alleviating stress and is an endeavour to stay calm. To stay calm is important: big oak trees grow from little acorns.

Positive thinking is a practice. It is something we should do everyday and as often, during the day, as possible. By practicing positive thinking everyday we create a state of mind whereby we become continually positive. Eventually we are able to create a tremendous amount of positive energy, an energy that will create positive situations for us everyday.

"Most folks are about as happy as they make up their minds to be."

(Abraham Lincoln)

In certain cases the medical profession now believe that having a positive attitude – that is practising positive thinking everyday – can improve our health. In fact, researchers found that having an optimistic outlook can do wonders for a patient's recovery – especially for those who have just gone through surgery. Researchers studied 16 patients over a 30-year period – examining their attitudes and recovery after surgery.

"In each case the better a patient's expectations about how they would do after surgery or some health procedure, the better they did", said author Donald Cole, of the Institute for Work and Health in Toronto.

SO HOW DO WE GO ABOUT IT?

How do we make positive thinking a part of

our daily lives? Actually it is quite easy, but discipline and practice is required.

Initially we must observe our thoughts and ourselves. It is surprising to see how many of our thoughts are positive and how many are negative. A good idea would be to keep a notepad handy and write down the positive thoughts, as and when they occur, and the negative thoughts, as and when they occur. At the end of the day count them up.

If you have more negative thoughts than positive then there's work to do.

On the following day, go through the same routine. Write down the positive thoughts and the negative thoughts and pay attention to the negative thoughts. What are they about? Are they making an impact on your life, in some way? Are they about the circumstances under which you live? Are they about your job? Are they about the distance you have to travel each day or week? Is there someone, within your life, causing you a lot of anguish?

Unfortunately, negative thoughts can make situations worse and create even more negativity, because thoughts are thought over and over again, until we believe them and they manifest. Positive thoughts repeated over and over again create a positive reality and they manifest within our everyday lives.

In the first instance we have to work on understanding our negative thoughts and what we believe and then begin to change them.

Once we begin to change them, we begin to create a positive attitude and this is when we get into the practice of positive thinking – everyday. We need to make positive thinking a way of life in order to get the most out of it.

So begin by getting rid of those negative thoughts, negative beliefs and negative situations, which do nothing except make us fed up and miserable. It is then and only then that we are able to start having a positive attitude and begin to enjoy life again.

There are techniques to help you to get rid of negative thoughts and start thinking in a positive way. It is a case of mind over matter and does get easier with practice. Positive thinking is a forceful energy (as forceful as negative thinking). Thinking in a positive way can create wonderful things within our lives.

Our present attitudes are habits, built up from listening to what others say; this could be from the feedback of parents, friends, society and self. These attitudes form our self-image and how we see the world. They are maintained by the inner conversations we constantly have within ourselves, both consciously and subconsciously.

The first step in changing our attitudes is to change our inner conversations.

You are what you think. You feel what you want.

WHAT SHOULD WE BE SAYING TO OURSELVES?

- ❑ I will make a POSITIVE Commitment to myself.
- ❑ I will take POSITIVE Control of my life.
- ❑ I can accept this POSITIVE Challenge.

Commitment

Make a positive commitment to yourself in respect of learning, in respect of your work, your family, your friends and anything that seems worthwhile to you. Do not be shy when it comes to giving yourself praise for a job well done when you achieve something positive. Always see success as an outcome within your mind. Be full of enthusiasm.

Control

Ensure that you keep your mind focused on the important things within your life. Set yourself goals and give yourself priorities for what you think and do. Visualise outcomes to practise your actions. Develop a policy for dealing with problems, as and when they arise. Learn to relax. Enjoy your successes and always be honest with yourself.

Challenge

Have courage in your convictions. Change and improve yourself each day. Do your best and don't look back. See learning and change as opportunities. Have a go at new things. Consider a variety of options. Meet new people. Ask lots of questions. Keep track of your mental and physical health. Be very optimistic.

It seems that studies have been made and show that people with these characteristics are winners in good times and survivors in hard times. Research shows:

'... people who begin consciously to modify their inner conversations and assumptions report an almost immediate improvement in their performance. Their energy increases and things seem to go better ...'

'The secret of achievement is to hold a picture of a successful outcome in mind.'

SETTING GOALS

Where In Your Life Would A Goal Be Helpful?

You can have any sort of goal. Common areas for goals include: health, financial, business, relationship/family, and more.

Sometimes it is obvious that something is not working in your life. If this is the case, focusing on what you would like that part of your life to be like, is an excellent place to start. Imagining a supportive network of family and friends or an extremely satisfying job that leaves you energised are great examples of such goals.

Other times, you just have a restlessness or uneasiness about your life. Often this is due to your life not being fulfilling. So perhaps having a goal that takes you the next step, or discovering other options, is the way to go.

How Do You Create Effective Goals?

Goals that pursue your passion really work. That is because often there is high (positive) emotion, desire, and strong images. Being able to picture a goal really does help it manifest.

Our experience has shown that having written goals, with dates, really helps the manifestation process.

Adding a picture, desire and work really makes it happen. Use your imagination!

Suggestions For Building Positive Attitudes

- ❑ If you go to an evening class, or any other type of class, look for positive people with whom to associate.
- ❑ With every lesson, look for one specific point of interest.
- ❑ In every book you read, find a point of interest in each chapter.
- ❑ Always ask your teacher a question.
- ❑ Tell your friends one item of interest you have just learned.
- ❑ Keep a list of all your goals, your positive thoughts and your positive actions.

Remember, you are what you think, you feel what you want.

Do you feel that your life is full or empty? Note your answer because it may show up your outlook and how you view situations. Do you see life in a positive or negative way?

VISUALISATION

It is said that many athletes use visualisation methods. Tennis players imagine their swing and location of their serve before they hit the ball. The footballer visualises the ball hitting the top corner of the net before he takes a penalty.

Visualisation is similar to a daydream, whereby we imagine scenes, conversations and actions in the movie of our mind. At the moment we daydream, the daydream may seem real to us. If we repeat the same daydream over a period of time it becomes a habit. We may even start to believe it and accept it as a reality, especially when strong emotions are involved.

When positive daydreams materialise, they can bring only good. Yet daydreams can also be about unpleasant events, about difficulties, trouble and self-pity. Then we call them worries. If we go on repeating them, they may materialise and bring us a lot of problems and unhappiness. Therefore, we should try to think in a positive way and have daydreams which bring happiness into our lives.

To visualise for a specific purpose you need a quiet, relaxed place. You begin by relaxing and working on clearing your mind – as in meditation. When you feel ready, follow up with about five minutes of visualisation. As you get used to doing this, you will improve and be able to increase your time, as well as become less distracted by noises or thoughts that will flit through your mind.

It is important to remember that the things we visualise affect our attitudes, moods and our state of mind. This means that we have to be very careful with what enters our mind. Thoughts are a bit like visitors, but when the same kinds of thoughts frequent the mind often, they become permanent residents. Do you accept and allow anyone to come and stay at your home? No? Then why do you let thoughts do that?

Deciding upon something that we really want to happen, and visualising it with concentration, faith and desire, sets energies into action, because visualisation is a powerful tool, which we need to know how to use correctly and in a positive way.

Creative visualisation is to create an image in the mind, and through natural laws cause it to manifest on the material plane. It is a natural process, which we all use, probably every day of our lives, though unconsciously. The thoughts that pass through our mind create our life, hence making them positive. It is possible to learn to accept only good and positive thoughts, and then go consciously through the process of visualisation, to fill our life with happiness, success and health.

A HEALTHY OUTLOOK

A study in the August 2002 issue of *Mayo Clinic Proceedings* reports that people who expect misfortune and who only see the darker side of life don't live as long as those with a more optimistic view.

Researchers evaluated results from a personality test taken by participants more than 30 years ago and compared them to subsequent mortality rates. They found that people who scored high on optimism had a 50 per cent lower risk of premature death than those who were pessimistic.

Besides a lowered risk of early death, researchers found other health benefits related to positive attitude. In the study, optimists reported:

- Fewer problems with work or other daily activities because of physical or emotional health.
- Less pain and fewer limitations due to pain.
- Less interference from physical or emotional problems when engaging in social activities.
- Increased energy.
- Feeling happier, calmer and more peaceful.

Researchers surveyed individuals in 1994 that had previously taken the Minnesota Multiphasic Personality Inventory (MMPI) at the Mayo Clinic between 1962 and 1965.

The 500-question personality test has an optimism-pessimism scale that grades the 'explanatory style' of the participants (how people explain the causes of life's events) and categorises them as optimists and/or pessimists or mixed, based on their answers to certain questions.

The results could lead to ways to help pessimistic people change their perceptions and behaviours and thereby improve their health and perhaps lengthen their lives, says Toshihiko Maruta, M.D., a psychiatrist at the Mayo Clinic, Rochester, Minn., and lead author of the study.

"It confirmed our common-sense belief", says Dr. Maruta. "It tells us that mind and body are linked and that attitude has an impact on the final outcome — death."

The researchers said they couldn't definitively explain how a pessimistic outlook acts as a risk factor for decreased longevity.

Dr. Maruta says optimists may be less likely to develop depression or 'learned helplessness', a condition that occurs when someone is exposed to repeated punishment or negative conditions and perceives no chance of getting away. Optimists also might be more likely to seek and receive medical help, seeing bad events as specific, temporary and controllable.

Optimism is a vital ingredient for a life that is creative, productive and enjoyable.

Research shows that optimists live longer, enjoy better health, and do better in relationships, work and sports. For some, optimism comes naturally. For most, it is an attitude towards life that must be learned and cultivated.

Pessimists, on the other hand, see life events negatively and expect the worst possible outcome. When bad events occur, pessimists often blame themselves and see problems as permanent and pervasive.

"It would help if they interpreted their negative experiences in such a way that they didn't blame themselves when things went wrong", Dr. Maruta says. "It also would help if they didn't think bad situations or experiences were going to last and realised that such circumstances often are temporary."

POSITIVE ATTITUDES AND AGEING

It is possible that having a positive attitude about getting older may affect your life as you age. If you want to live for a long time and your life to be filled with vitality, fun and social functions, these basic beliefs can shape your future for the better. However, if you live totally convinced that growing old means a life full of depression and sickness, this may lead to finding yourself experiencing a mental problem that could lead to physical debilitation.

The August 2002 issue of the *Journal of Personality and Social Psychology* reports that older individuals who viewed ageing in a positive light lived 7.5 years longer than those who had a negative view of ageing.

HAVE FUN: A HEALTHY HABIT FOR HEALTHY AGEING

Naturally, all our lives have a certain number of challenges and frustrations within them and it is up to us to look for ways to improve our contentment and enhance our overall well-being. We can do a number of things to experience pleasure.

Aerobic exercise releases endorphins, which are substances that produce feelings of satisfaction and wellness. Satisfaction and a feeling of well-being will reduce stress, depression and anxiety. It can also give us a feeling of accomplishment whilst reducing tetchiness and anger.

To eat well is very important too. Our body and mind need good nutrition to run efficiently. Eating a diet rich in fruits, vegetables and grains can improve the way you feel.

Get plenty of relaxation. Sleep refreshes us. It improves our attitude and gives us the energy for physical activity and also enables us to cope with stress.

TAKE CONTROL

Eliminating stress and the conflicts in our lives can be exciting. Identify the area or areas of our lives that cause us the most stress, and then simplify those areas.

Get organised. Taking control of our lives may be just what we need to feel happy. Do all you can to get your life organised and as free of chaos as possible.

Now, take a step back. Write down all the good things in your life. If your list is short, add a section of new goals you'd like to achieve. Focus on being satisfied with your life as it is. Remember, your health depends on it.

Chapter 7

Stress Management

What is Stress?

It is normal to be stressed at times, during our lives, but it is not a good thing and we should learn to manage it. It is possible to do so. Stress is a type of pressure, which we may not always be able to eliminate, but we can react sensibly and control our thought process, which would allow us to relieve the pressure. I was once told that the secret is to act, not react, in a stressful situation.

Stress can be an exceptionally negative influence within our lives and it can come from most areas of our lives causing feelings of rejection, anger, distrust of others and sometimes ourselves, making us indecisive. It can cause headaches, rashes, sleepless nights, high blood pressure and heart disease, which could lead to a stroke. Often stress occurs when we have to readjust our lives in some way.

Our reactions to stress are triggered by our perception of physical or emotional danger and if we aren't careful we exaggerate it within our minds. We may look at a difficult situation in the wrong way and handle it badly because we haven't given it enough thought. Sometimes we are inclined to over react and see things as urgent, when they may be anything but urgent. Sometimes we feel terrible because we cannot please everyone, or we allow ourselves to feel guilty and sometimes in trying to please everyone we please no one and make ourselves feel ill or become ill. Many of us just have to learn to say one little word – NO! Which for some unknown reason we find impossible to say.

It is important to try to view our stress related problems to work out the possibilities of coping with them, or at least get them out of total confusion and into some semblance of order which we can control. Now and then the answer may just be a case of walking away from the situation. Though, depending on what it is, it is wiser to see if there is another way around the problem before we do. Now and then there is one important way to put it right and that is – communication.

So how do you learn how to manage the stress within your life? One way would be to learn how to cope by learning about stress and how to handle it and the other is to try not to get into the situation in the first place. Often this is easier said than done, because this type of situation can pop up when we least expect it and take us by surprise. However, once within our lives we can learn to recognise it quickly and become efficient in our way of handling it.

To help alleviate stress, there is the visualisation method, which we've just covered in this book, together with the meditation method and positive thinking. These are three ways to set you up and help you to get back your control. These will help tremendously. It has to be remembered that peaceful thoughts induce relaxation and stressful thoughts induce stress.

Everything is connected with our thought process and this is obviously going to influence us all the way down the line. The way we present ourselves to others, the way we feel inside, our health and so on. We do not have to be victims.

Sometimes, stress can add excitement to our lives and we need a little of it to thrive, so we are not trying to eliminate it, just control it. If there was no stress at all we would probably become bored or fed up. Therefore, we need motivation but do not need to be overwhelmed and unable to relax.

So, stress management is the key. We have to learn how to change anxiety to concern. To take care of our problems, to be aware of our feelings, to be able to work out what is upsetting us and how to cope with it – manage it.

Work out your stress problems. If necessary make a list of them and then set some goals as to how you are going to manage them, so they stop managing you. Try to remember that life is to be enjoyed and no one has the right to make you feel otherwise. So resume control, stay calm and smile.

Learning how to relax our mind and body can be invaluable in stress relief. Below you will find instructions on using relaxation and meditation techniques.

LEARN RELAXATION TECHNIQUES

Make a note of how you sit at the table. Are your shoulders hunched up? Are your hands relaxed? Do you ever catch yourself clenching your teeth? Do you tap your foot or your fingers when you are sitting with nothing to do? Do you twiddle your thumbs? Do you notice yourself fidgeting or feeling tight, even when you're sitting still. Any of these mean that you are probably not relaxing enough.

Stress and being anxious about things can interfere with our ability to concentrate, so it is very important that we take the time to relax, or meditate.

One way to relax is to try and shut out the world, if only for five minutes. You can do this by either lying down or sitting in a comfortable position and then by closing your eyes.

Now concentrate on each area of your body. Are you tense? Do you ache? Imagine this tenseness or your ache gradually melting away.

A good way to do this is to begin at your toes and work your way up through your feet, ankles, legs, knees, and thighs and on to each section; your hips, buttocks, waist, back, shoulders, neck, head, arms to wrist, hand to fingertips and then the muscles in your face.

Concentrate on your breathing. Breathe slowly, regularly and deeply.

When you feel relaxed, imagine you are walking, sitting or lying in a place of beauty, full of peace and quiet.

After five or 10 minutes, open your eyes and rouse yourself gradually.

MEDITATION

There are various forms of meditation, three of which are detailed below.

Meditation 1

The first is in respect of the Life Force, which is a healing energy. When this flows freely within us there is health and well-being.

There are five steps for this Healing Meditation. The major focus is your breathing. Concentrate on slowly inhaling and exhaling. Feel calm and allow your thoughts to come and go without focusing on them too much.

1. Sit as straight as possible and close your eyes.
2. Breath slowly, inhale, exhale, as silently as possible.

3. As you inhale imagine that you are breathing in this Life Force, picture it as light.
4. As you exhale, gently direct this light energy to the area you are concerned about. If no particular area, then imagine the light (Life Force) going through your body.
5. Continue until you feel you have breathed in enough Life Force.

Meditation 2

This meditation is specifically to calm your inner self and to maintain your balance in any given situation. It is excellent in respect of stressful situations.

There are four steps:

1. Sit comfortably, with your eyes closed, keeping your spine reasonably straight.
2. Try to ensure your attention rests on your breathing.
3. When sounds, thoughts, emotions or any kind of physical sensations arise, simply acknowledge and accept them, allowing them to pass without getting involved with them.
4. If you suddenly realise that your attention has wandered into thinking, emotional

issues or sensations, such as an itch, bring your attention back to your breathing and continue with your meditation.

Meditation 3

This meditation develops concentration and visualisation. It is a colour meditation and is begun by sitting comfortably with closed eyes.

- ❑ Visualise a huge ball of Golden light resting a few inches over your head.
- ❑ Visualise it as descending through your crown, so that your entire body is filled with Golden light.
- ❑ Imagine your body absorbing that Golden light as it cleanses and heals you.
- ❑ Repeat, visualising a ball of Red light.
- ❑ Repeat, visualising a ball of Orange light.
- ❑ Repeat, visualising a ball of Yellow light.
- ❑ Repeat, visualising a ball Green light.
- ❑ Repeat, visualising a ball of Blue light.
- ❑ Repeat, visualising a ball of Indigo light.
- ❑ Repeat, visualising a ball of Violet light.

Go through the colours in your own time, own pace and then visualise yourself in a state of perfect, radiant health.

Chapter 8

Herbs to Help your Memory

SAGE

New research has proved that sage can improve memory, confirming centuries-old theories. British scientists have carried out the first clinical trials with healthy, young adults and found that those who had taken sage oil capsules performed significantly better in a word recall test.

The team, from the Medicinal Plant Research Centre (MPRC) at the Universities of Newcastle and Northumbria, have provided scientific evidence for claims dating back centuries.

They studied texts by well-known herbalists such as John Gerard, who wrote about sage in 1597, saying that 'It is singularly good for the head and brain and quickeneth the nerves and memory', and Nicholas Culpeper, whose 1652 text says, 'Quicken the senses and help Memory'.

People were known to take sage for memory loss centuries ago and drank teas and tinctures containing extracts of the herb.

The Newcastle team tested 44 healthy young adults aged between 18 and 37. Some were given capsules containing sage oil and others were given placebos.

The volunteers then took part in a word recall test and were tested at intervals to see how many words they could remember. Results showed that those who had taken the sage oil consistently performed better than those who had taken placebos.

Sage is being investigated as a potential treatment for Alzheimer's disease after earlier research by the MPRC found that it inhibits an enzyme called acetyl cholinesterase (AChE), which breaks down the chemical messenger, acetylcholine. Alzheimer's', the most common form of dementia which affects an estimated 10 million people worldwide, is accompanied by a drop in acetylcholine.

Researcher Nicola Tildsley stated the results

of the study proved that, in some cases at least, the herbalists should be taken seriously. She added, "This proves how valuable the work by the old herbalists was, and that they shouldn't just be ignored because they were writing centuries ago."

ROSEMARY

According to Nicholas Culpeper, rosemary is also good for the 'weak memory'.

Herbalists use rosemary to treat dizziness due to inner ear problems, nerve conditions, headaches, halitosis, stomach ailments and as pain-reducers. Ancient folk remedies list it as a memory-enhancer. Since rosemary is such a flavourful addition, it is a staple to those on a salt-restricted diet.

WARNING: Essential, distilled rosemary oil, (not to be confused with flavoured cooking oils), should never be taken internally. It is poisonous in strong doses. Be sure to consult your doctor before attempting any medicinal use of any herb, spice or other home remedy.

Appendix

The Philosophers of Memory

c.510–c.450 BC **Parmenides**, Greek philosopher
Parmenides believed that a memory was a type of description or re-enactment of a past experience. His doctrines influenced Plato.

429–347 BC **Plato**, a Greek philosopher
Plato was deep into dualism.....perception vs. reason as sources of knowledge and perception vs. memory.

It is easy to think of our own minds as containing a memory store and a separate processor that can produce thought by being able to manipulate what is stored in memory.

Plato divided the process of thought into four parts: object, perception, conceptualisation, and form.

384–322 BC **Aristotle**, Greek philosopher and scientist

Aristotle wrote over 400 books on every branch of learning, including logic, ethics, metaphysics, biology and psychology.

c.460–370BC **Democritus**, Greek philosopher and scientist

His atomism considered that all matter consists of minute particles – atoms– which account for different properties of matter apparent to our senses.

205–70 AD **Plotinus**, Greek philosopher

Idea of the perfection of the soul as involving a process by which the soul loses memory of wordly experience and becomes only concerned with pure, abstract thoughts.

1685–1753 **Berkeley**, George, Irish bishop and idealist philosopher

Representative of modern philosophers debating the role of experience in the production of knowledge. Perception producing Memory, which is then available in thought as a source of knowledge.

1711–76 **Hume, David**, Scottish philosopher and historian

A Treatise of Human Nature (1739–40)

Distinctions discussed between memory and imagination in terms of degrees of vividness of the thoughts. Hume argued against the Absolute Truth of empirical knowledge.

1788–1860 **Schopenhauer, Arthur**, German philosopher

The World as Will and Idea (1818)

Process by which brains construct our view of external reality is mostly an unconscious response to sensory organ activity that leads us to only be aware of what is seen, not the process by which we see.

"Happiness is good health and a bad memory."
(Ingrid Bergman)

Other Books from Windsor

Vinegar, Nature's Secret Weapon – Our No.1 bestseller. Use vinegar for health and around the house PLUS Honey and Garlic bonus sections.

Clean Your Liver – Help your body's 'detox machine' improve your health.

The Diabetics Guide to Healthy Living – Improve blood sugar levels, boost energy, feel 100% better.

How to Relieve the Pain of Arthritis – The latest breakthroughs and information all sufferers should have!

Unblock Your Arteries – How to beat Britian's No.1 killer.

The Sciatica Relief Handbook – natural ways to prevent flare-ups.

Stopping Restless Legs Syndrome – millions sleep easy again with these natural remedies.

Alternative IBS Treatments – practical solutions for IBS problems.

The Complete Guide to Tinnitus and Deafness – tried and tested remedies for lasting relief.

Improve Your Eyesight – exercise, diet and great tips to improve your eyesight.

Relief from Psoriasis – get relief for psoriasis and prevent further flare-ups.

Fibromyalgia Relief Handbook – Don't suffer in silence. Get all the facts and latest treatments.

The Gout Relief Handbook – find out which foods help keep gout away. Plus all the latest treatments.

Back Pain? How to Stop it – beat back pain with the latest methods.

The Potent Man – improve virility and regain your libido.

Foot Infections Handbook – keep troublesome foot and nail complaints at bay.

The Rosacea Handbook – new remedies and how and why they work.

Grow New Hair – Contrary to popular belief, balding and hair loss can be reversed.

Hydrogen Peroxide: for your Health and for your Home – astonishing uses around the home – and for your health.

Prostate Problems – essential reading for every man aged 45+.

Garden Magic – hundreds of tips for a beautiful garden.

Free for Seniors – get your share of the millions on offer from the government.

Government Cash Benefits Handbook – find out how much money the government owes you.
